TOTAL Eclipse
Or Bust!

A Family Road Trip

DEDICATION

For my granddaughters, Valerie and Maggie, the motivating forces behind this book. They give my life a special purpose.

For my Grandmother Anna, who inspired me in many ways. In 1910, she held her first baby up toward the heavens one night so he could say he had seen Halley's Comet.

For anyone who has never seen a TOTAL Solar Eclipse. I hope this book will inspire you to make the journey into the path of totality on August 21, 2017, and other times as well. If this story convinces you that totality is an event not to be missed, then I have accomplished the mission I chose.

TOTAL Eclipse or Bust! A Family Road Trip

Astropixels Publishing
P.O. Box 16197
Portal, AZ 85632

Astropixels Publishing Website: *astropixels.com/pubs*

This book may be ordered at: *astropixels.com/pubs/TEOB.html*

Printed in the United States of America

ISBN 978-1-941983-07-2

Astropixels Publication: AP008

First Edition

Front Cover Photo: *Eclipse Trio* – A total eclipse of the Sun is embraced by two *Diamond Rings**, signaling the beginning and end of totality (Lake Hazar Turkey, August 11, 1999).
Photo copyright ©2015 by Patricia Totten Espenak. More images of this eclipse can be seen at: *www.mreclipse.com/main/photoindex.html#solar*

Back Cover Map: Courtesy of Michael Zeiler, *GreatAmericanEclipse.com*

*See Glossary on page 34.

TOTAL Eclipse Or Bust!
A Family Road Trip

by Patricia Totten Espenak
graphic design by Fred Espenak

Prologue

A *total solar eclipse** is one of the most awesome sights in nature. On average, a particular spot on Earth experiences this event only about once every 375 years.

A total solar eclipse occurs *somewhere* on Earth about every two years. But all too often, much of the eclipse path is over the oceans or in countries where travel is difficult or impossible because of war, weather or poor roads.

However, on **August 21, 2017**, a total solar eclipse will sweep across the United States, and there are many places to see it that are easy to reach.

If you are thinking, "What's so great about a total solar eclipse?" or "Why do I need to go where the eclipse is *total*?" then I would ask you to name some place in the world that you think is a spectacular sight. You might say, "The Grand Canyon."

Now imagine that the Grand Canyon is only visible every two years, and only for 2 or 3 minutes each time. Would you try to be there to see it? And just think, if you didn't go, you would have to wait two years for another chance! And even if you went, you might miss it because of dense fog or rain.

With that in mind, take a road trip through space and time for an amazing adventure with a spectacular ending.

Seeing a total solar eclipse is an unforgettable experience, and it's all about being in the right place at the right time!

*See the Glossary on page 34 for more information about this and other terms marked with an asterisk.

The Road Trip Begins . . .

Two little girls sat very still under a tree in their yard and looked at each other. They were puzzled. They had never seen their Grammy so excited before. This must be a very special trip she had planned. She had been talking about it for years, but they still weren't exactly sure what it was all about. Now the time had come, and they were almost ready to leave.

Maggie turned to Valerie and said, "Where do you think we're going? I know Grammy said something about an eclipse, but *where* is an eclipse?"

Just then, Grammy came outside.

"Where is an eclipse?" Valerie asked.

"Oh, an eclipse can be anywhere on Earth," Grammy answered. "You just have to be in the right place at the right time."

"But where are *we* going?"

"We are going to travel into the future!"

"Oh, that's silly," Valerie said. "We're always traveling into the future. We can't help it. Now if we were going into the past, that would be exciting!"

"Well, I promise you, this will be a very exciting trip—one of the most exciting trips you will ever take. A *total solar eclipse**, when the Sun is completely hidden by the Moon, is such a wonderful thing to see that I've traveled all over the world just to see one."

"Really, the *whole* world?" Maggie exclaimed.

"Yes," Grammy said. "Grampy and I have gone to all seven continents to see a total eclipse, even to Antarctica! But this time, we won't have to go that far. The eclipse path goes from Oregon all the way across the country to South Carolina, like a big banner across more than 10 states. There are lots of places to go, and all you have to do is get in the car and drive."

---

*See the Glossary on page 34 for more information about this and other terms marked with an asterisk.

Just then, Mom, Dad and Grampy came out of the house. "Is everyone ready?" Mom asked. "Are you excited?"

"We'd better get started, because we have to drive for 2 days to get there," Dad reminded everyone.

Once they were in the car and on their way, Valerie asked, "But why do we have to be on the road for 2 days, Grammy? I heard it's going to be a 70 percent eclipse right here. Isn't that good enough? Couldn't we just stay home?"

"Oh, no! Even 99 percent isn't good enough. It's like the difference between looking at a picture of an ice cream cone and *eating* an ice cream cone. They are not the same at all. We *have* to see 100 percent. **TOTAL Eclipse Or Bust!**"

"Where are *we* going to go, Grammy?" Valerie asked.

"There are so many places, that Grampy and I had a hard time deciding, and we still might have to change our plans at the last minute because of the weather. While we're driving, look at the map I brought. A spot anywhere within the **yellow** path will do, and if the weather is good, we will see the total eclipse."

Path of the Total Solar Eclipse of August 21, 2017

"A lot of people won't have to travel for 2 days like we do," Grampy said. "Some may be just a few hours from the path. And many people live *in* the path. They don't need to go anywhere. Remember, close does NOT count! You have to be inside the **yellow**!"

"TOTAL Eclipse Or Bust!" Grammy reminded.

"Just look at these two pictures," Grampy said. "That's the difference between a *partial eclipse** and a total eclipse! The partial is interesting, but the total is awesome."

Grampy continued, "Very few people in the United States have ever seen a TOTAL solar eclipse. The last time one passed over any of the lower 48 states was almost 40 years ago, way back in 1979."

"I can't wait to see *this* total eclipse," Grammy said to the girls. "I have been waiting for this one for a long time, and I especially want to see it with the two of you."

Grampy added, "Thousands of years ago, people watched the Sun, Moon and stars much more than we do today. For example, they would keep track of the Sun in the spring, as it moved farther and farther north so they would know when to plant crops. They watched and studied the heavens because their lives depended on knowing about such things."

"What did people think back then, when an eclipse happened?" Maggie asked.

"Eclipses were very scary events many years ago because no one knew what caused them," Grampy said. "Can you imagine how people must have reacted when it suddenly got dark, right in the middle of the day, with almost no warning, and all that was left was what looked like a hole in the sky?"

Grammy added, "They might have thought that all the Sun's light was going to disappear right through that hole."

"Or maybe they thought the Sun would go away and never return—that the world would be dark forever! So they would do things like bang on drums and shout until the Sun came back. And you know what? It always worked!" Grampy said with a smile.

"Of course, the Sun would have come back anyway. But people believed that shouting and making noise would scare away the monster who was eating the Sun," Grammy said. "Sometimes they would even hide inside their houses and miss the whole thing, but we know better today."

"What else did they do, Grammy?" Valerie asked.

"There are many stories about how people in ancient times reacted to total eclipses. One of them tells how some American Indians believed that a solar eclipse meant the fire in the Sun was going to go out. Of course, they wanted to keep the fire going, so they would shoot burning arrows at the Sun to try to keep it lit."

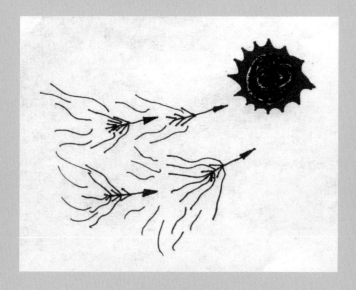

"Let's stop for lunch and talk about some more eclipse legends. Here's a spot with lots of trees for shade. Do you think this would be a good place to watch a total eclipse?" Grampy asked.

"Well, it would be nice and cool in the summer, but the trees sure wouldn't let you see the Sun very well," Valerie said.

"That's right," Grammy agreed. "There are so many things to think about when you pick a spot to view the eclipse. Sometimes even mountains can get in the way if the Sun is low in the sky."

Grampy continued talking about the legends. "In Japan, they would hang a necklace of precious stones on the branches of a tree. Because the stones were shiny, they were supposed to make up for the light lost when a solar eclipse occurred."

"How do you think these trees would look with lots of fancy necklaces hanging on them?" Dad asked. "What a sight that would be! I don't think those necklaces would make up for the light lost from the Sun though. Do you think they would bring the Sun back?"

"Well, you know the Sun would come back anyway, Dad," Valerie said.

Grammy continued, "In some countries in Africa, the Sun and the Moon were thought to be fighting during an eclipse. No one wanted to lose the Sun or the Moon, so the people would try to do good deeds for each other to encourage the Sun and the Moon to stop fighting. I like that story because it brought people together instead of scaring them. It's always better to be kind than to fight about things, don't you think?"

"I like that story, too, Grammy. And you always say that the most important thing is to be kind," Maggie answered.

Grampy continued, "One of *my* favorite stories is about the Chinese, who thought that a dragon was swallowing the Sun. They would set off fireworks and make as much noise as possible to frighten the dragon away and bring back the Sun. I like that story because I like dragons!"

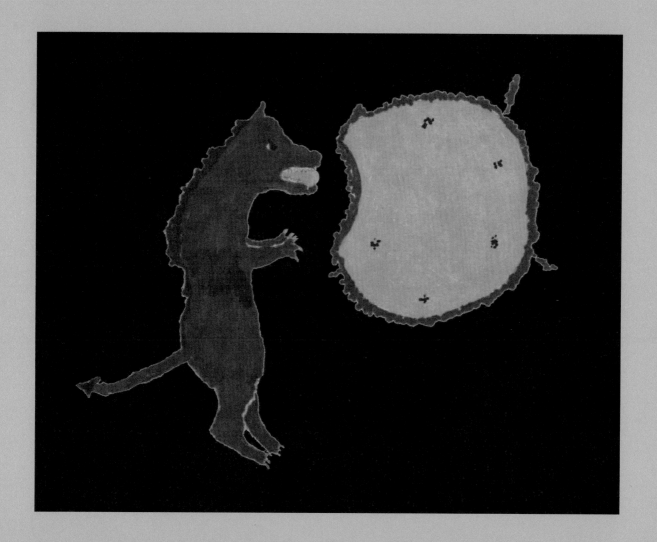

"Well, we're done with lunch, so let's pack up our stuff and hop in the car," Mom said. "We still have a long way to go."

As they continued down the road, Valerie asked, "Grammy, when did you see your first eclipse?"

"Well, it took a long time before I saw my first total eclipse, but it turned out for the best. Back in 1970, even before your Mom was born, I planned to see my first one. My chance came in March, but some friends talked me out of going. It was a beautiful day, but at home we only saw 95 percent—not good enough. I was so close!"

"Remember," Grammy said, "you want to taste the ice cream, not just look at a picture of it! Even if you can *see* a real ice cream cone, if you're not close enough to lick it, you certainly can't taste it. Close isn't good enough. **TOTAL Eclipse or Bust!**"

"And look over there," Grammy said. "There's a picture of Grampy at that very same eclipse. He didn't let anyone talk *him* out of going! And he was so amazed by it, that he started chasing eclipses all over the world."

"Why didn't you go with *him*, Grammy?"

"Well, I didn't know him then or I probably would have, but I didn't give up. On my next try we went to Canada, but we were *clouded out.** Your mom was just a baby, but that was her first eclipse. It took two days to drive there, just like our trip now. And even though there were clear skies in places that we could have reached, we just didn't know about them. We didn't have a backup plan, a Plan B. We'll talk more about *that* later, but right now, look at *totality** flanked by two *Diamond Rings** in the picture below. I took those pictures in Turkey in 1999."

8

Fred Espenak observes
the total solar eclipse
of March 7, 1970
from Windsor,
North Carolina.

Then Mom said, "Almost 20 years later, Grammy, Uncle Russ and I went to Hawaii, but we were clouded out there, too."

Grammy added, "So you shouldn't pass up any chance to see totality—to see the Sun completely hidden during the daytime. You never know when *your* next opportunity will come. Because I passed up that wonderful chance in 1970, it took 25 years and a trip halfway around the world to India before I finally saw a total eclipse."

"That's a really long time, Grammy," said Valerie as she looked out the window at the hills going by.

"Yes it is. And by the time I got to India, I had been disappointed so many times that even though the Sun rose in a beautiful clear blue sky on eclipse day, I was convinced I would miss it again. I was the only person in our group who had never seen a total eclipse, so everyone was very excited for me."

"You're making me excited, too," Maggie exclaimed.

"Well, I hope so!" Grampy said. "I want you to be at least as excited as you are about ice cream. And just look at this beautiful picture I took in India that day. The string of bits of sunlight around the bottom of the Moon's black disk is known as *Baily's Beads**."

Then it was time to stop for dinner. Grammy said, "I'll tell you the rest of the story about the India eclipse when we get back into the car."

"Grammy, that's a real cliff hanger!" Maggie said.

"I *am* getting hungry though," Valerie agreed.

"Me, too," said Dad. "Let's stop and take a break. It's been a long day."

"Yes," Grampy said. "I'm hungry, too. Remember, tomorrow will be a shorter trip, and when we stop for the second night we will be in the path of totality!"

Brilliant beads of sunlight shine through valleys on the Moon's edge as the total eclipse of October 23, 1995 begins in Dundlod, India.

Back in the car after dinner, Grammy continued, "So that day in India, we all waited anxiously for the moment when the Sun would disappear completely behind the Moon. I thought I was ready for that moment, but I wasn't. It was truly awesome! The total eclipse was so beautiful it made me cry. I wasn't scared, but I was overcome by the darkness, the sounds of people yelling, dogs barking and the most amazing sight I had ever seen. I wrote a poem about that day. It goes like this.

REMOTELY CLOSE

In another life, the Moon
Touched me with his dark shadow,

Blocked the Sun,
Revealed her crown.

Now that image, impossible to imagine,
Draws me to the next chosen place,

Where the Moon's shadow sword
Will nick the Earth again.

"Right away I asked, 'Where's the next one?' and I've been chasing eclipses ever since. There was a bonus to that eclipse, too, because that's where I met Grampy. If I hadn't gone halfway around the world to see something that lasted only 41 seconds, we probably never would have met."

Then Grammy listed her rules for eclipse chasing.

1. Don't let anyone talk you out of going.

2. Go every time you can.

3. Always have a backup plan, a Plan B.

4. **TOTAL Eclipse Or Bust!**

"And about that Plan B," Grampy told them, "that's why you have to watch the weather. Don't forget, Grammy was clouded out twice, and I've been clouded out, too. So you can pick your spot, but always have a second place in mind. If the weather is going to be cloudy where you are, get in the car the night before the eclipse and drive to a sunnier spot. That's real eclipse chasing!"

"Do *we* have a Plan B, Grampy?" Valerie asked.

"Of course! We are going to watch the weather just like I said. And we might change our direction tomorrow if our Plan A spot looks cloudy or rainy. We just have to keep an eye on where the clouds are."

"Grammy, are we there yet?" Maggie asked.

"Well, we have arrived where we are going to stay for our first night. It's been a long day, so let's get a good night's sleep. Then we'll have lots of energy for our trip into the path tomorrow."

"But Grammy, I'm so excited I'm not sure I can go to sleep. I can't wait for the eclipse!" Valerie said.

"I can't wait for the eclipse either!" Grammy agreed.

Over the River and Through the Woods . . . to Totality!

When morning came, Grammy and Grampy were up first. After breakfast Dad said, "Come on everybody. We have to hit the road. The eclipse won't wait for us to get there."

Once they were all back in the car and headed down the highway, Grammy brought out another picture to show everyone.

"Here's an amazing photo Grampy took in Africa in 2001. Look, you can actually see the Moon in front of the Sun. Isn't it beautiful?"

Then Grammy told the girls, "You might think eclipse chasing is something new, but people have been predicting and chasing eclipses for hundreds of years."

"You mean even before *you* were born, Grammy?"

"Oh, yes. In 1918, almost 100 years ago, there was an eclipse with a path similar to this one in 2017. It went from Oregon across the country to Florida."

Grampy added, "One astronomy group sent a team to observe the eclipse in Oregon. They prepared for a whole year and went to their location more than a month early. They wanted to be sure they had enough time to get ready."

Grammy continued, "Color photography hadn't been invented yet, so they took along an artist to paint the eclipse. He had less than 2 minutes to get his impressions down, so that later he could paint what he remembered. Why don't you draw a picture of what you think the eclipse is going to look like, based on pictures you've seen? Then you can compare it to what you really see."

by Valerie

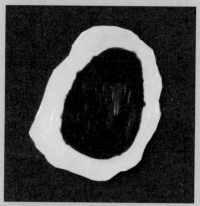
by Maggie

"But even when people saw a painting, if they hadn't seen a total eclipse with their own eyes, they just couldn't believe that it looked so strange and amazing," Grampy said. "So, it was important to get a good photograph, too. Many people tried to do that, but it wasn't easy with the film and cameras they had back then. Finally, someone managed to capture a photograph of a total eclipse. How exciting that must have been."

15

Grampy continued, "The first black and white photograph of a total eclipse was taken way back in 1851. Here it is."

"And you know what else?" Grammy asked. "People who chased eclipses years ago had a hard time for many reasons. Sometimes the maps they used weren't very good, and even wars could interfere. In 1780, an eclipse expedition was sent out from Harvard College in Massachusetts during the American Revolution, and they had big problems."

Grampy added, "Yes, people were chasing eclipses even during wartime! In this case, the British agreed to let the scientists work unharmed, but after all their efforts, they missed the eclipse because they were outside the path of totality. Their map of the eclipse path was *wrong*!"

"They must have been so disappointed," Valerie said.

"I'm sure they were. At least *we* won't have *that* problem," Mom replied.

Then Grampy said, "One of the most interesting eclipses in history was in 1878. It's sometimes called the Pike's Peak Eclipse, but it also has stories about a chicken coop and a mysterious planet named Vulcan."

"Oh, now you're just kidding us!" Valerie said.

"No, I'm not. Astronomers were very interested in this eclipse because it passed over Pike's Peak in the Rocky Mountains, where the thin air at the mountaintop was expected to provide *good seeing**."

"Tell us about the chicken coop, Grammy."

"That's quite a funny story. Thomas Edison, a famous inventor, was in Wyoming for the eclipse and decided to set up his equipment in a chicken coop to escape the wind and dust. As he was getting ready in the doorway, right before totality, the chickens came home to roost. Feathers went everywhere! Those chickens thought night was falling. I'll bet Edison was surprised!"

"But what about that mysterious planet called Vulcan?"

"Here's what happened with that part of the story," Grampy said. "At another place in Wyoming, there were problems besides chicken coops. They had a complicated plan to search for Vulcan. We know now that Mercury is the planet closest to the Sun, but back then they thought there was a planet that was even closer. Supposedly, this planet, Vulcan, had been sighted before, but astronomers were not sure, and no one knew exactly *where* to look. If it did exist, they thought it could easily be found during a total eclipse."

"What did they do?" Valerie asked.

"They decided that if Vulcan were sighted in Wyoming, they would send a telegram to Dallas, Texas, telling exactly where they saw the planet. Then a rider on horseback would take the telegram and gallop out to an observing site about a mile away so those observers could look for Vulcan in the same place around the Sun, to confirm that they saw it, too. They didn't have a lot of time to do it!"

Grammy added, "The astronomers in Wyoming thought they had spotted Vulcan, but in all the excitement they forgot to send the telegram, so the astronomers in Texas didn't know where to look. For the next 50 years the search for Vulcan continued, but the planet was never found. Now we know there is no such planet, but it's still exciting to think about that search. And it just goes to show you, even astronomers can get so amazed by a total eclipse, that they forget what they are supposed to do!"

"But you said it was called the Pike's Peak eclipse, didn't you, Grampy?" Maggie asked.

"Yes, there was also an expedition to Pike's Peak, and they had a very tough time. They reached the top of the mountain 9 days before the eclipse, but their tents didn't arrive until 3 days later. They had to climb an 18-mile footpath with all their equipment to get to the top. Some things even had to be left behind. And while they were waiting, they had high winds, hail, rain, sleet and snow. But they had clear weather on eclipse day, so you just never know!"

"Even though there were photographs from as far back as that one in 1851," Grammy said, "drawings still gave some of the best information about what an eclipse looked like. Just look at this drawing made during the Pike's Peak eclipse."

Grampy added, "And here's a twist from yet another eclipse. Many years ago, scientists thought of an eclipse as a chance to discover the Sun's secrets, because that was the only time they could see the *corona**, the Sun's beautiful 'crown'. Helium, that gas in all your party balloons, was discovered *in the Sun* at an eclipse in 1868! Imagine that, something that was first discovered in the faraway Sun. It was named helium from the Greek, 'helios,' which means Sun. It was not found here on Earth until about 25 years later!"

HARPER'S WEEKLY.

A JOURNAL OF CIVILIZATION.

Vol. XXII.—No. 1130.]   NEW YORK, SATURDAY, AUGUST 24, 1878.   [WITH A SUPPLEMENT. PRICE TEN CENTS.

Entered according to Act of Congress, in the Year 1878, by Harper & Brothers, in the Office of the Librarian of Congress, at Washington.

THE GREAT SOLAR ECLIPSE.—Sketched at Snake River Pass, Colorado, by St. George Stanley.—[See Page 675.]

"We're here at last," Mom announced as they arrived at the campground where they were going to stay. "The eclipse is tomorrow. Let's have something to eat and go to bed."

During dinner Grammy asked, "Do you know how many total eclipses I've seen? Sixteen! Grampy has seen even more."

"But why have you gone to so many, Grammy? Isn't one enough?" Valerie asked.

"Is one ice cream cone enough? Is one flavor enough? Not for me! Each eclipse is different, not just in how long it lasts, but in what it looks like. And sometimes, *where* you see an eclipse can make a big difference, too."

"Were you ever scared like those people in the legends?" Maggie asked.

"Oh, yes," Grammy said. "That happened one year when we visited a village in Africa. The village was only a few huts with dirt floors. We gave out solar filter glasses and showed the villagers how to use them. Our interpreter explained that it would get dark and the Sun would disappear for a few minutes. We thought if we explained what was going to happen, they wouldn't be afraid."

"Back at our camp, about a mile away, we waited," Grampy continued. "The Moon's shadow swept over the village before it got to us. In spite of our explanation, they were still scared. We heard their terrified screams and then *we* were plunged into the shadow!"

"Of course, *we* knew what was going to happen, but it was still one of my scariest moments ever, just hearing those screams," Grammy said. "But it was also a gorgeous sight. I will never forget it. Now get some sleep, because tomorrow the Moon's shadow will sweep over you!"

Then Maggie said, "I'm so excited, I *really* don't think I'm going to be able to get to sleep now!"

"We'll just close our eyes and count sheep," Valerie suggested.

So everyone climbed into their sleeping bags and started counting.

Eclipse Day!

The next day, Grampy and Dad woke up very early. They made breakfast, and after everyone finished eating, they all checked the map again.

"Can you find where we are?" Grampy asked. "Just remember, we must be inside the **YELLOW** path, and the farther from the edges we are, the longer totality will last. Are we at a good place? Yes!"

"The weather looks clear, so we'll stay right here. I don't think we'll need our Plan B," Grammy said.

Path of the Total Solar Eclipse of August 21, 2017

More detailed maps can be found at the back of this book. For additional maps of your destination go to **eclipsewise.com/solar/SEnews/TSE2017/TSE2017.html**

As they got out their solar eclipse glasses and found a good place to sit, Grammy said, "What a beautiful day! This reminds me of that first eclipse I saw in India, when the sky was so clear and blue. Now we just have to be patient."

"How much longer?" Maggie asked.

"Oh, it won't be long now," Grammy said. "And while we're waiting, here's something incredible, that I haven't told you before. We are very lucky, because we live in a Solar System with an unusual coincidence. The Sun is 400 times bigger than the Moon, but it is also 400 times farther away from Earth. This means the Sun and the Moon appear just about the same size in the sky. So when an eclipse happens, the Moon can just exactly block the Sun. It's an amazing coincidence that makes total solar eclipses so spectacular."

"What really makes an eclipse happen, Grammy?" Valerie asked.

"Well, the Sun makes the Moon cast a shadow, just like it makes our shadows in the daytime. When the Moon is between Earth and the Sun this shadow points in the direction of Earth. But sometimes the Moon is too high and its shadow passes above Earth and sometimes it is too low and its shadow passes below Earth. In those cases, the shadow just stretches out into space."

Grampy added, "Look at these diagrams and imagine the Sun is far away off to the left. You can see how the Moon can be too high or too low for its shadow to hit Earth."

"And this is what happens most of the time," Grammy said. "So even though the Moon passes between Earth and the Sun every month, we don't get a total eclipse every month. When the Moon's shadow misses Earth completely, there is no eclipse."

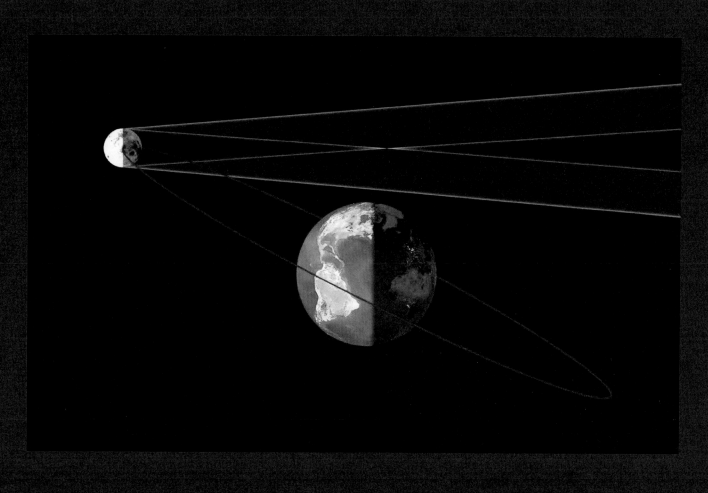
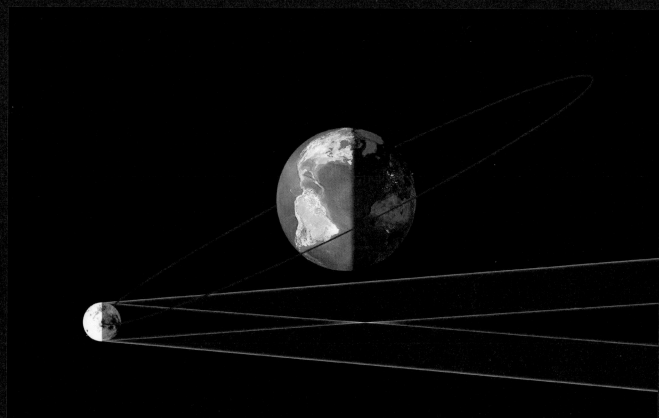

"But," Grammy continued, "just like in 'Goldilocks and the Three Bears,' once in a while the Moon is not too high and not too low—everything is *just right*. It is exactly between Earth and the Sun. At those times, the Moon's *umbra** sweeps across Earth and we have a total eclipse."

"What's an umbra, Grammy? You didn't mention that before."

"The umbra is the dark part of the Moon's shadow—the part that gets smaller as it gets closer to Earth. That's what you have to be *inside* to see the total part of the eclipse. If you're in the bigger, lighter part of the shadow you will only see a partial eclipse. It's easy to remember, because 'umbra' is related to the word 'umbrella,' and an umbrella casts a shadow, too. But that diagram doesn't begin to tell the story."

"We know, we know. **TOTAL Eclipse Or Bust!** We want to taste the ice cream!" the girls cheered.

"Are we going to have ice cream on eclipse day, Grammy?" Maggie asked.

"Oh yes, let's do that," Valerie chimed in.

"What a great idea. I'll see if I can arrange it."

The girls got quiet for a while because they knew the eclipse was coming soon. What would it be like? Would they cry like Grammy did? Would they be a little bit scared? What would they remember? Would it be awesome?

They almost jumped out of their skin when Grampy started talking again.

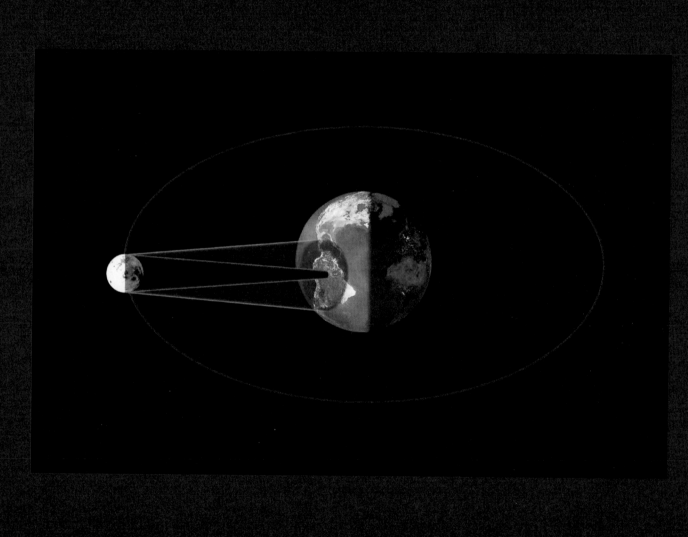

"Get ready. The eclipse will start in a few minutes," Grampy said. "Remember, when the Moon blocks only part of the Sun it is **not safe** to look without protecting your eyes. Put on these solar filter glasses and look at the Sun before the eclipse begins."

"But Grampy, I can't see anything. It's all black!"

"That's because the Sun is so powerful that the glasses have to be very dark to make them safe. Keep them on and look toward the Sun. Move your head around slowly until you see a bright disk. Doesn't the Sun look tiny?"

When the partial eclipse was about to begin, Grammy said, "Try to see when the Moon takes that first little 'bite' out of the Sun. Then you can understand why people thought something was eating the Sun. The bite will get bigger and bigger for quite a while, so just take a look about every 5 minutes. That will be enough to see that things are changing."

Then Grampy reminded everyone again, **"Do not look at the Sun without your solar filter glasses until totality begins!"**

"How will we know when it's time to take them off?"

"It will get dark and maybe even a little chilly. People around you may be yelling. Believe me, you will know!"

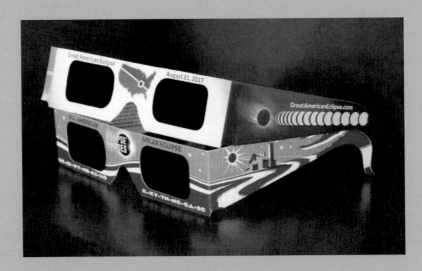

Sample solar filters. For more on eye safety go to
eclipse.gsfc.nasa.gov/SEhelp/safety2.html

"When totality is over," Grammy said, "you could write something to remember what it felt like. I say 'felt,' because it is more than something you see. Here's a haiku I wrote on another trip, to try to capture the experience."

TOTAL ECLIPSE

Chilling dark descends.
Rendezvous of rushing spheres,
Crashing soundlessly!

As they sat and waited, the light began to change. "It's almost time. Can you feel it getting darker and cooler?" Mom asked.

"This is the exciting part. It will seem like it's over in only a few seconds, so look as hard and as fast as you can! Look for that 'hole' in the sky. It's almost as if you can see the Moon move. Look! There's the *Diamond Ring** and now totality! Take off your solar filter glasses. Isn't it beautiful?" Grammy asked.

They watched as the corona surrounded the black disk of the Moon. The girls let out a big, "Oh!" It seemed like time stood still. There really was a "hole" in the sky. They looked around and saw the horizon was glowing pink in all directions. Then they heard crickets chirping, and a dog really did bark.

It seemed like it was just after sunset, even though the Sun was high in the sky. No wonder those chickens came home to roost!

After what seemed like only a few seconds, a tiny bead of sunlight appeared along the Moon's edge and quickly grew very bright. The total eclipse was over.

"And now we're back in the sunlight—way too soon! Time to put your solar filter glasses back on if you want to look at the Sun," Dad said.

"What did you think?" Grammy asked.

"Oh, Grammy, it really *was* awesome!"

"Did you think it looked like a hole in the sky? How did you feel?" Mom asked. "You might want to write something down before you forget. Maybe you'll even write a poem of your very own."

"Right now I just want to try hard to remember what it was like. It was over so fast!" Valerie said.

"I wasn't ready!" Maggie sighed.

"It's kind of sad when it's over, don't you think? But aren't you glad we came?" Grammy asked.

"Oh, yes! I'm so glad we came all the way," Valerie exclaimed. **"Total Eclipse Or Bust!"**

"Me, too!" said Mom and Dad and Grampy.

"Me, too!" said Maggie. "Can we have ice cream now?"

"Yes, we'll get ice cream, but the eclipse isn't completely over yet. The Moon is slowly moving off the Sun now, and the Sun will get brighter and brighter. After the excitement of totality, the final partial phases are much less interesting, but I always watch off and on until the end," said Grammy. "And then, of course, I ask the question, 'Where's the next one?'"

"Where *is* the next one, Grammy?"

"Well, the *very* next one is in July, 2019 way down in South America, and most of the path is out in the Pacific Ocean. *And* it's winter down there then and it's a long way to go. So you can see that eclipse chasing is not always this easy. But we are lucky because there is another total eclipse through the United States in April, 2024."

"Can we go to that one, too?"

"Of course. Let's pick a spot right now. Grampy has the map."

Path of the Total Solar Eclipse of April 8, 2024

The girls looked at the map and thought about where they might go next time. Texas? Ohio? Maybe even Canada or Mexico. The adventure would continue.

(NOT) THE END!

EPILOGUE

TOTAL Eclipse Or Bust!

We took a crazy road trip,
A trip that was a "must."

We even had a motto,
"Total Eclipse Or Bust!"

We went to watch the Sun go out,
It was a sight to see.

And now we know how great it is,
To taste Totality!

For me, a total eclipse brings to mind this quote from Wordsworth:
"Poetry is the spontaneous overflow of powerful feelings: it takes its origin from emotions recollected in tranquility."

May you find the tranquility to recollect the powerful emotions that I hope a total eclipse brings to you. And perhaps even write a poem of your own.

Clear skies!
Patricia Totten Espenak

GLOSSARY

Baily's Beads Brilliant bits of sunlight that shine through deep valleys on the edge of the Moon right before and after totality.

Clouded out The expression used when clouds obscure the Sun, so the eclipse cannot be seen.

Corona The atmosphere of the Sun. The beautiful feathery halo that is only visible from Earth during a total solar eclipse.

Diamond Ring The last bit of sunlight that shines through a very deep valley on the edge of the Moon right before and after totality.

Good seeing When the atmosphere is stable and/or at high altitudes where the atmosphere is thin and does not interfere with astronomical observations.

Partial solar eclipse A solar eclipse in which the Moon's disk covers only part of the Sun. Eye protection must be worn when viewing a partial solar eclipse.

Total solar eclipse A solar eclipse in which the Moon's disk completely covers the Sun and the corona is visible. Every total eclipse begins and ends with a partial eclipse.

Totality The part of a solar eclipse when the Moon completely covers the Sun. This is the **only** time when it is safe to look without solar filters.

Umbra The dark, inner shadow of the Moon. You must be inside the umbra to see totality.

ACKNOWLEDGMENTS

A very special thanks . . .

To Teri Bellows, my fellow teacher and co-conspirator in many things, and my Circuit Writer buddies, Carolyn Dearing and Gerry Hernbrode, who all helped polish things up at the end.

To my children, Andrea and Russell, who put up with my many, <u>many</u> queries for input and editing. They each have seen one total solar eclipse and I hope will see many more. And to my super editor, Valerie, who found all the mistakes missed by everyone else!

Most of all, to my husband, Fred, whom I first met in the Moon's shadow more than two decades ago and half a world away. Without his assistance in putting this book together, it would never have come to fruition. He has more patience than anyone who doesn't live with him could ever know.

Photo and map credits
Patricia Totten Espenak – cover, title page and pages 2, 8, 24, 25, 26, 27, 29, 31
Fred Espenak – pages 4, 9, 11, 14, 23, 25, 27, 29, 31, 37
Valerie – pages 7 and 15
Maggie – pages 5 and 15
Michael Zeiler – back cover map and maps on pages 3, 19, 21 and 32, GreatAmericanEclipse.com

The author in 2003 at Davis Station, Antarctica

Patricia Totten Espenak is a retired chemistry teacher who has traveled widely with her husband, Fred, to view various celestial events, including Total and Annular Solar Eclipses, Lunar Eclipses, and Transits of Mercury and Venus. She has traveled to 16 Total Solar Eclipses on all seven continents. Between packing and unpacking, she enjoys hiking with Fred in the Chiricahua Mountains of Arizona near their home, skiing at Lake Tahoe with her son, Russell, and his husband, Warren, and spending summers on Long Beach Island, New Jersey, with her daughter, Andrea, son-in-law, Mike, and granddaughters, Valerie and Maggie.

The following three pages contain more detailed maps of the 2017 eclipse path.

At various points along the path you will find information about that part of the path. The key to this information is as follows.

In the first example (above the path in Oregon):

10:20am PDT
(This is the time of mid-totality—the middle of the total eclipse in Pacific Daylight Time)

2m 03s
(The length of totality at this point in the path.)

41°
(The height of the Sun at mid-totality.)

For additional maps of your destination go to:

eclipsewise.com/solar/SEnews/TSE2017/TSE2017.html

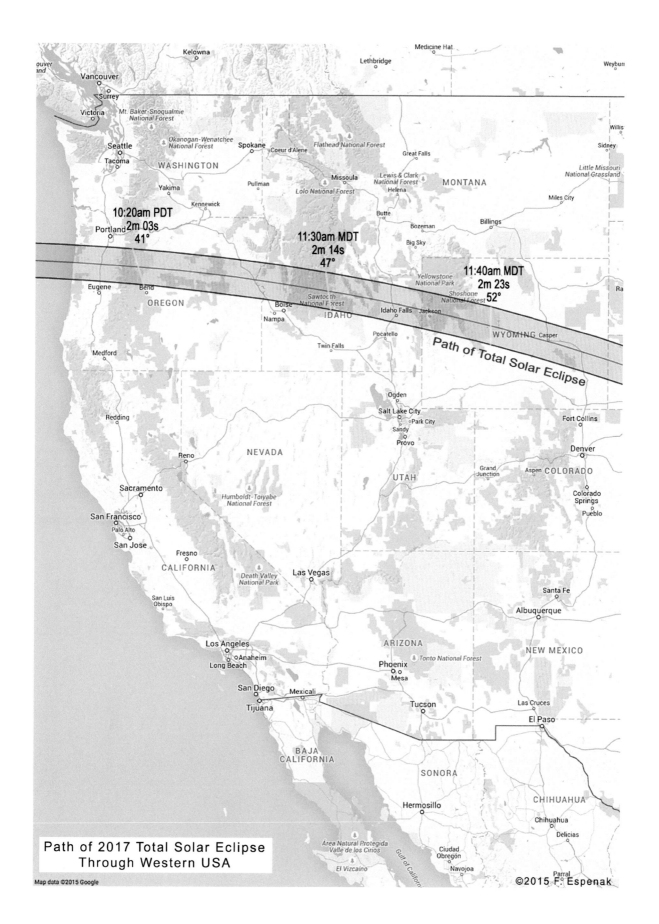

Labels on map:

10:20am PDT
2m 03s
41°

11:30am MDT
2m 14s
47°

11:40am MDT
2m 23s
52°

Path of Total Solar Eclipse

**Path of 2017 Total Solar Eclipse
Through Western USA**

Map data ©2015 Google

©2015 F. Espenak

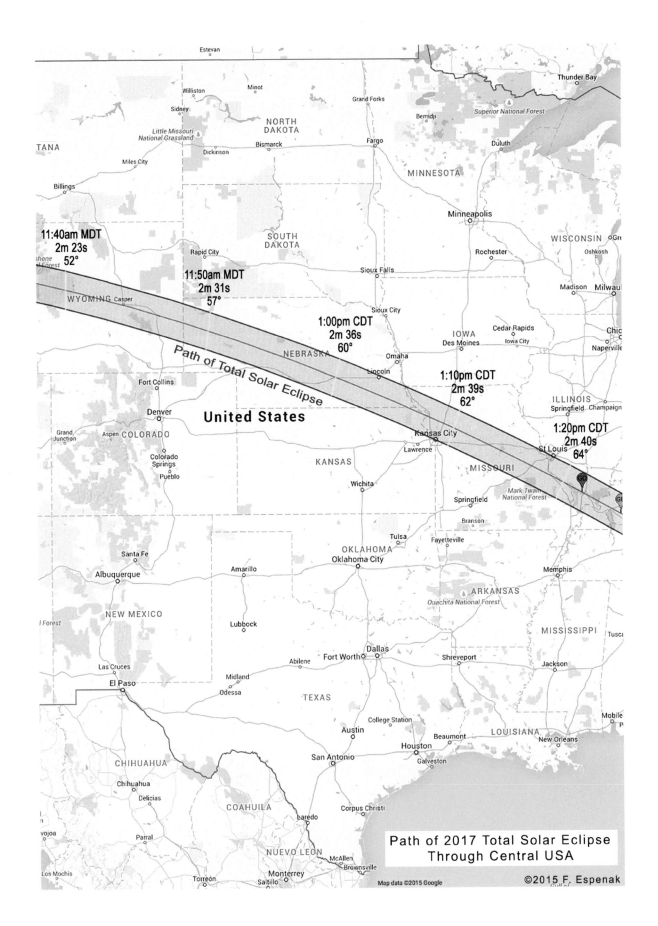

Path of 2017 Total Solar Eclipse
Through Central USA

©2015 F. Espenak

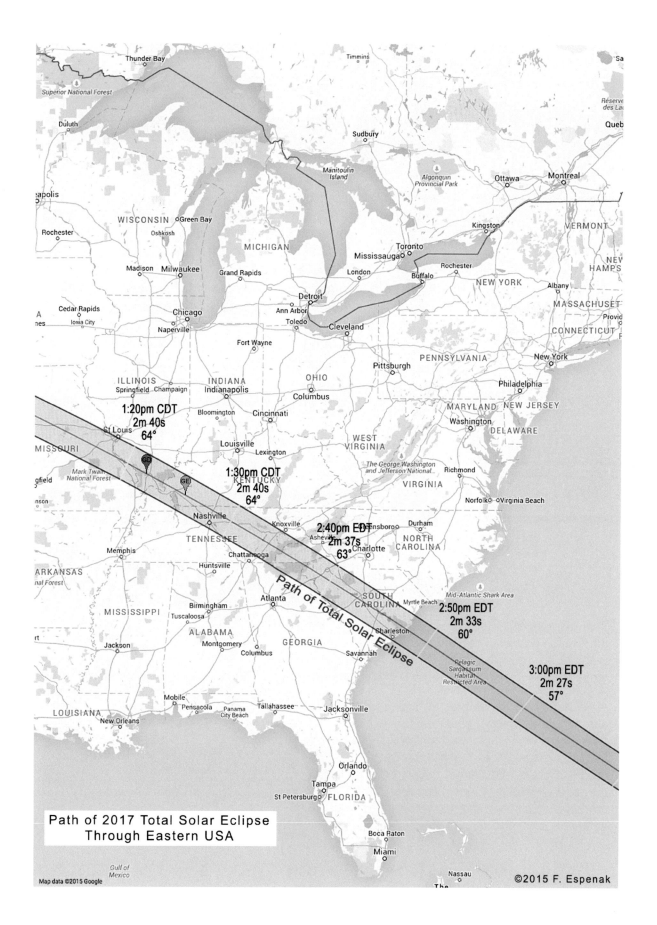

1:20pm CDT
2m 40s
64°

1:30pm CDT
2m 40s
64°

2:40pm EDT
2m 37s
63°

2:50pm EDT
2m 33s
60°

3:00pm EDT
2m 27s
57°

Path of Total Solar Eclipse

Path of 2017 Total Solar Eclipse
Through Eastern USA

Map data ©2015 Google

©2015 F. Espenak

41

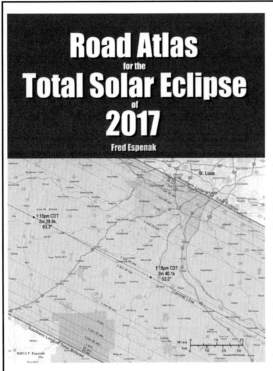
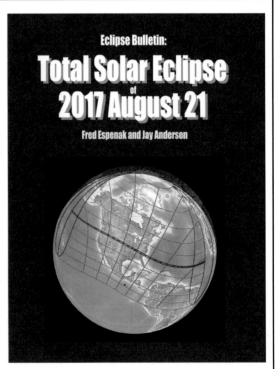

37523321R00030